Before We Open Presents

Kristi Dusenbery

Printed in the United States of America

ISBN 978-0-578-31108-1

Library of Congress Control Number: 2021921516

The Laughing Grandma
Indianola IA 50125

www.TheLaughingGrandma.com

Dedicated to
our kids and grandkids

May you always be too excited to sleep the night before Christmas
and always be filled with joy because of Jesus.

Long before Christmas
was ever a thing;
Long before shepherds
heard angels sing,

**God knew
your name.**

And he already loved you so much.

So much,
that he made a perfect plan
just for you!
He'd send baby Jesus,
to grow into a man;
to save you completely
like no one else can.

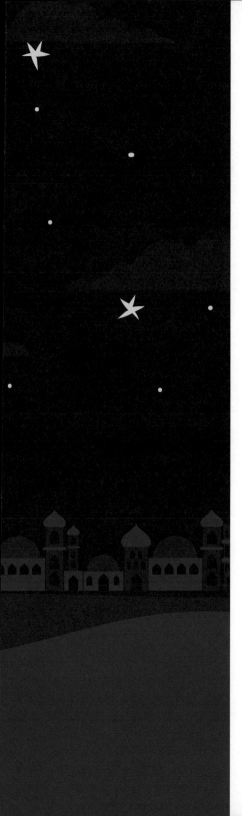

But who would raise Jesus
with love and with truth?
Who would be perfect?
Who would God choose?

From the start of the world,
He already knew...

A strong man named Joseph,
who worked hard all his life.
And a kind girl named Mary
who would soon be his wife.

At last it was time,
to tell them the news.
So an angel came down,
with this message of truth:

"You have found favor,
you're God's chosen ones.
And you will be parents

to God's only Son."

These words were a shock,
and they both felt afraid.
But they trusted God's promise
and continued to pray.

Many months later,
they had to leave home
for the census of Rome.

So, they packed up their donkey
and traveled long roads,
'til they finally reached Bethlehem

tired and alone.

So far from home,
it was time to give birth.
No family. No friends.
No room at the inn...
Just a smelly old stable
with cattle and hay,
a smelly old feed-box,

**but this
was the day.**

Soon Jesus arrived,
without fanfare or style.
And God must have
been watching,

**with such a
big smile.**

Mary kissed her son's face
and wrapped him up tight;
there in the stable,
in the dark, silent night.

Not too far away,
lay some shepherds
and sheep...
resting on hills
with barely a peep.

When all of the sudden
an angel appeared,
in the light of God's glory,
to share with the shepherds
the first Christmas story:

**"A Savior is born
to Joseph and Mary!"**

The shepherds jumped up,
to follow God's star.
They walked, then they ran...
It was all so bizarre!

At last
there they stood,

Silent

with tears in their eyes,
as the first Christmas carols
filled the night sky.

Soon came three wise men
with gifts wrapped in gold.
And they

fell to their knees

...a sight to behold.

Mary smiled
and Joseph looked on,
amazed by God's promise
revealed in their son.

And you know what?

That first Christmas night,
I think God's smile grew

**as he thought
about you**

because he already knew
that Jesus would love you,

forgive you

and make you

brand new.

So remember this Christmas,
as you open your gifts
and play with your toys,
that the very

best present

is God's precious boy...
born in a manger
to fill you with joy!

Jesus wants to make you new:

The wrong things you do keep you far from God.
Everybody sins. Sin is when we choose to do, think, or say things that we know are wrong. The Bible says that our sin separates us from God and causes him to turn away from us.
Isaiah 59:2

Jesus made a way for your sins to be forgiven.
Jesus chose to die on the cross, to take the punishment for our sins. But he didn't stay dead. He came back to life to live in heaven with God and he wants us to live there someday, too. The Bible says that Jesus carried our sins in his body on the cross...and we are healed because of his wounds. 1 Peter 2:24

God wants you to accept his free gift of forgiveness.
To receive his free gift, we can pray and tell God that we are sorry for our sins, we believe Jesus died to forgive us, and that he lives to make us new. The Bible says, if we say out loud that Jesus is Lord and believe in our heart that God raised him from the death, then we will be saved. Romans 10:9

Dear God,

I know that I have done bad things and I'm so sorry.
I believe that Jesus came to earth as a baby, lived a perfect life, and died on the cross to forgive my sins. I also believe that he came back to life so I can go to heaven someday.
I want you to be part of my life and I want to be in your family. Please help me to do what the Bible says and help me to make good choices every day. Thank you so much for Jesus!
Amen

Now what?

- Be excited! Jesus has washed away your sin and you are part of his family!
- Read the Bible and ask God to help you make good choices.
- Spend time with other people who are in God's family by going to church.
- Be thankful every day for all of the good things and for every good promise God gives you.

The First Christmas Story:

Before the world was made, God loved you: Ephesians 1:5

And before the world was made, God decided to make us his own children through Jesus Christ. That was what he wanted and what pleased him.

An Angel Talks to Mary: Luke 1:26-32

God sent the angel Gabriel to a virgin who lived in Nazareth, a town in Galilee. She was engaged to marry a man named Joseph from the family of David. Her name was Mary. The angel came to her and said, "Greetings! The Lord has blessed you and is with you." But Mary was very confused by what the angel said. Mary wondered, "What does this mean?" The angel said to her, "Don't be afraid, Mary, because God is pleased with you. Listen! You will become pregnant. You will give birth to a son, and you will name him Jesus. He will be great, and people will call him the Son of the Most High. The Lord God will give him the throne of King David, his ancestor.

An Angel Talks to Joseph: Matthew 1:19-21

Mary's husband, Joseph, was a good man. He did not want to disgrace her in public, so he planned to divorce her secretly. While Joseph thought about this, an angel of the Lord came to him in a dream. The angel said, "Joseph, descendant of David, don't be afraid to take Mary as your wife. The baby in her is from the Holy Spirit. She will give birth to a son. You will name the son Jesus. Give him that name because he will save his people from their sins."

The Birth of Jesus: Luke 2:1-7

At that time, Caesar sent an order to all people in the countries that were under Roman rule. The order said that they must list their names in a register...So Joseph left Nazareth, a town in Galilee. He went to the town of Bethlehem in Judea...Joseph went there because he was from the family of David. He registered with Mary because she was engaged to marry him.

Shepherds Visit Jesus: Luke 2:8-19

That night, some shepherds were in the fields nearby watching their sheep. An angel of the Lord stood before them. The glory of the Lord was shining around them, and suddenly they became very frightened. The angel said to them, "Don't be afraid, because I am bringing you some good news. It will be a joy to all the people. Today your Savior was born in David's town. He is Christ, the Lord. This is how you will know him: You will find a baby wrapped in cloths and lying in a feeding box." Then a very large group of angels from heaven joined the first angel. All the angels were praising God, saying: "Give glory to God in heaven, and on earth let there be peace to the people who please God."

Then the angels left the shepherds and went back to heaven. The shepherds said to each other, "Let us go to Bethlehem and see this thing that has happened. We will see this thing the Lord told us about." So the shepherds went quickly and found Mary and Joseph. And the shepherds saw the baby lying in a feeding box. Then they told what the angels had said about this child. Everyone was amazed when they heard what the shepherds said to them. Mary hid these things in her heart; she continued to think about them.

Wise Men Visit Jesus: Matthew 2:1-2

Jesus was born in the town of Bethlehem in Judea during the time when Herod was king. After Jesus was born, some wise men from the east came to Jerusalem. They asked, "Where is the baby who was born to be the king of the Jews? We saw his star in the east. We came to worship him."

God sent Jesus to save us: John 3:16

God loved the world so much that he gave his only Son (Jesus). God gave his Son so that whoever believes in him may not be lost, but have eternal life.

*These scriptures are from the International Children's Bible

About the Author

KRISTI DUSENBERY has a Master's Degree in Education and lives in Indianola, Iowa, where she is a teacher and instructional coach, and authors *The Laughing Grandma blog* She and her husband Tim were married in 1988 and love spending time with their three sons, three daughters-in-law and six grandkids. Oh, and two very spoiled dogs.

When entering the "parenting adults" stage of life, Kristi became suddenly aware of how unprepared she was to navigate those new waters without drowning herself or anyone else. Not only did she find herself swimming in the deep end, she and her husband often struggled to agree on the best way to proceed. The years that followed became a quest to understand what it truly means - and if it's even possible - to become a woman who is *clothed with strength and dignity, able to laugh without fear of the future* (Proverbs 31:25). Bits and pieces of her ongoing journey are posted on *The Laughing Grandma* blog and Facebook page, where she shares her passion for the responsibility grandmas have to shine the joy of Jesus into the lives of their families. No gimmicks. No hidden agenda. Just honest talk about how to thrive as wives, moms, and grandmas.

To join the journey, stop by **www.TheLaughingGrandma.com** and follow **@thelaughinggma** on Facebook.

Made in United States
Troutdale, OR
12/03/2023